This notebook belongs to

ONE DIRECTION

centum

Published 2013. Centum Books Ltd.
Unit 1, Upside Station Building Solsbro Road,
Torquay, Devon, UK, TQ26FD

books@centumbooksltd.co.uk

Contents

All About Me

Name: ....

Age: ....

Birthday: ....

Star sign: ....

Email: ....

Hair colour: ....

Eye colour: ....

Height: ....

Signature: ....

School: ....

Tutor Group: ....

My fave pic of me!

I ♥ HARRY
LIAM
LOUIS
NIALL
ZAYN

Now & Then

It is the start of a new term and a fresh school year lies ahead waiting for you to jump in. The One Direction story shows how much can happen in just a few years. From dreaming of stardom, to meeting new best friends, forming a mega successful band and then conquering the world – the 1D journey so far has been amazing!

When I first saw them, I thought ....
....
....
I loved ....
the most.

Now when I look at them, I think ....
....
....
Now I love ....
the most.

I ♥ ONE DIRECTION

'It's amazing to think back to when we were first put together – and to the point we are at now. Things have moved so quickly, it's got all of us in a massive state of shock. It's so surreal to think of everything – like winning the BRIT, doing our first UK tour, having our first number one. I can't believe all of this has happened to us five lucky guys. We love our fans and owe all our success entirely to them – we want them to know that.'

Liam

9

'A dream is only a dream until you decide to make it real.'

HARRY STYLES

Harry

I ♥ HARRY

Fact File:

Name: *Harry Styles*
Birthday: *1st February 1994*
Star Sign: *Aquarius*
Height: *178cm (5ft10)*
Eye colour: *Green*
Born in: *Holmes Chapel, Cheshire, England*
Twitter: *@Harry_Styles*

Gorgeous and multi-talented Harry is the youngest in the band. Not only does he speak French and play the kazoo, he can also juggle – a very useful talent for someone with so much going on! Harry loved Maths and P.E. at school but used to get told off for chatting in class. Naughty Harry!

The things I love most about Harry are...

'Dreams are like stars – you may never touch them, but if you follow them, they will lead you to your destination.'

LIAM PAYNE

I ♥ LIAM

Fact File:

Name: *Liam Payne*
Birthday: *29th August 1993*
Star Sign: *Virgo*
Height: *178cm*
Eye colour: *Brown*
Born in: *Wolverhampton,*
West Midlands
Twitter: *@Real_Liam_Payne*

Lovely Liam is a true romantic with a secret talent for beatboxing. He says that he's too shy to flirt, but that only adds to his charm. His nickname is Daddy Directioner as he is the most mature in the group. Liam's fave subject at school was P.E. and he excelled at running, basketball and boxing.

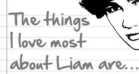

The things
I love most
about Liam are...

TEXAS
TRAVEL TRAIL

'The fact that we can make people happy from what we love doing is incredible.'

LOUIS
TOMLINSON

Louis x

I ♥ LOUIS

Fact File:

Name: Louis Tomlinson
Birthday: 24th December 1991
Star Sign: Capricorn
Height: 175cm
Eye colour: Blue
Born in: Doncaster, South Yorkshire
Twitter: @Louis_Tomlinson

I ♥ 1D

Super-talented Louis can play the piano and has four younger half-sisters to boss around! He appeared in lots of productions while at school including *Grease*, showing that he was a star in waiting. Before he hit the big-time on *The X Factor*, Louis tried life as an actor and even appeared in *Waterloo Road*.

The things I love most about Louis are...

15

'Being single doesn't mean you're weak, it means you're strong enough to wait for what you deserve.'

NIALL HORAN

I ♥ NIALL

Fact File:

Name: *Niall Horan*
Birthday: *13th September 1993*
Star Sign: *Virgo*
Height: *171cm*
Eye colour: *Blue*
Born in: *Mullingar, Ireland*
Twitter: *@NiallOfficial*

Gorgeous Niall is proud of his Irish heritage and has the colours of his country's flag stuck to the bottom of his microphone. Niall showed his talent in the school choir; he hated Maths but loved French. His teachers thought he was in a world of his own. Maybe, he was dreaming of super-stardom!

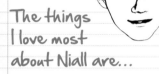

The things I love most about Niall are...

17

'Life is a funny thing, the minute you think you've got everything figured out something comes along and turns it all upside down.'

ZAYN MALIK

Fact File:

Name: *Zayn Malik*
Birthday: *12th January 1993*
Star Sign: *Capricorn*
Height: *175cm*
Eye colour: *light brown*
Born in: *Bradford,*
West Yorkshire
Twitter: *@ZaynMalik*

This lovable lad has loads of talents including being able to draw and play the triangle. He is super brainy too and loves reading. Zayn's fave subject was English and he even landed an A at GCSE! Although he can't swim and is scared of the dark, his sensitive side only makes us love him more.

The things I love most about Zayn are...

Amazing Albums

If you focus on what you want to achieve and keep working nothing can stop you.

One Direction's debut album, *'Up All Night'*, went to number one in 17 countries. An amazing success! The album was recorded in Sweden, the UK and the US and released in Autumn 2011.

What Makes You Beautiful
Gotta Be You
One Thing
More Than This
Up All Night
I Wish
Tell Me A Lie
Taken
I Want
Everything About You
Same Mistakes
Save You Tonight
Stole My Heart

My fave song from the album is ....
....
because ....
....
....

Loads of super-cool writers and producers wanted to work with the boys. The lucky ones included writer Rami Yacoub (who has worked with Britney, Bon Jovi and Backstreet boys), producers Steve Mac (Westlife, JLS), Red One (Lady Gaga, JLo), Carl Falk (Akon, Taio Cruz, Backstreet Boys) and Toby Gad (Beyoncé, Alicia Keys, Fergie).

ONE DIRECTION
UP ALL NIGHT

In the Mix...

1. **Which song was written by Kelly Clarkson?**
....

2. **Which songs did 1D write themselves?**
....
....

3. **How many tracks are on the album?** ....

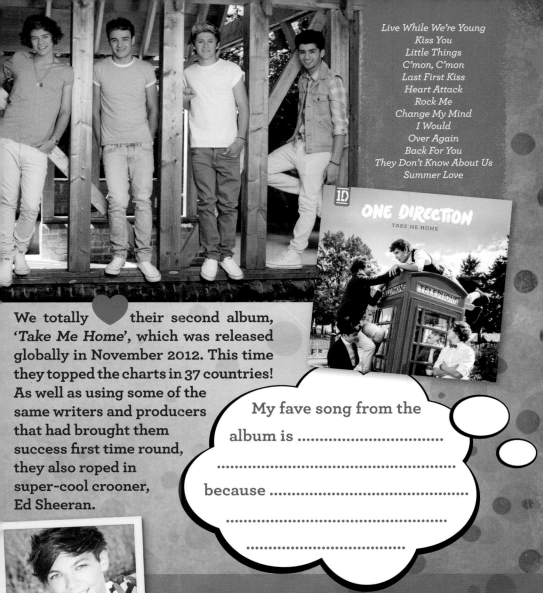

Live While We're Young
Kiss You
Little Things
C'mon, C'mon
Last First Kiss
Heart Attack
Rock Me
Change My Mind
I Would
Over Again
Back For You
They Don't Know About Us
Summer Love

We totally ❤ their second album, **'Take Me Home'**, which was released globally in November 2012. This time they topped the charts in 37 countries! As well as using some of the same writers and producers that had brought them success first time round, they also roped in super-cool crooner, Ed Sheeran.

My fave song from the album is .... because ....

'I want people to listen to it and say, "Wow, is that One Direction?". It's not too cheesy – I think it's the kind of album that guys will like as well as girls.'
Louis

My Planner

2013

Time to make sure you are super organised for the year ahead. It's going to be a busy one! Not only do you have to juggle school work, time for your family and chillin' with your besties, you also need to keep track of those all-important 1D dates.

I ♥ HARRY

September

M	*Back to*	2	9	16	23	30
T	*School!*	3	10	17	24	
W		4	11	18	25	
T		5	12	19	26	
F		6	(13)	20	27	
S		7	14	21	28	
S	1	8	15	22	29	

October

M		7	14	21	28
T	1	8	15	22	29
W	2	9	16	23	30
T	3	10	17	24	31
F	4	11	18	25	
S	5	12	19	26	
S	6	13	20	27	

I ♥ NIALL

I ♥ LOUIS

November

M	4	11	18	25
T	5	12	19	26
W	6	13	20	27
T		7	14	21	28
F	1	8	15	22	29
S	2	9	16	23	30
S	3	10	17	24	

December

M	2	9	16	23	30
T	3	10	17	(24)	31
W	4	11	18	25	*Christmas*
T	5	12	19	26	
F	6	13	20	27	
S	7	14	21	28	
S	1	8	15	22	29

2014

January

M		6	13	20	27
T	*Happy*	7	14	21	28
W	*New Year!*	1	8	15	22	29
T	2	9	16	23	30
F	3	10	17	24	31
S	4	11	18	25	
S	5	(12)	19	26	

I ♥ ONE DIRECTION

I ZAYN

22

February

M	3	10	17	24
T	4	11	18	25
W	5	12	19	26
T	6	13	20	27
F	7	♥14	21	28
S	①1	8	15	22
S	2	9	16	23

March

M	3	10	17	24	31
T	4	11	18	25	
W	5	12	19	26	
T	6	13	20	27	
F	7	14	21	28	
S	1	8	15	22	29
S	2	9	16	23	30

April

M		7	14	★21	28
T	1	8	15	22	29
W	2	9	16	23	30
T	3	10	17	24	
F	4	11	Easter ★18	25	
S	5	12	19	26	
S	6	13	20	27	

May

M	★5	12	19	★26
T	6	13	20	27
W	7	14	21	28
T	1	8	15	22	29
F	2	9	16	23	30
S	3	10	17	24	31
S	4	11	18	25

June

M	2	9	16	23	30
T	3	10	17	24	
W	4	11	18	25	
T	5	12	19	26	
F	6	13	20	27	
S	7	14	21	28	
S	1	8	15	22	29

July

M		7	14	21	28
T	1	8	15	22	29
W	2	9	16	23	30
T	3	10	17	24	31
F	4	11	18	25	
S	5	12	19	26	
S	6	13	20	27	

August

M		4	11	18	★25
T		5	12	19	26
W	Summer 6	13	20	27
T	Holidays! 7	14	21	28
F	1	8	15	22	㉙29
S	2	9	16	23	30
S	3	10	17	24	31

I ♥ LIAM

Key

★ Bank Holidays

◯ 1D Birthdays

23

Write Your Own
Song

What will you discover about yourself this year? Time to test your song-writing skills! A song combines poetry and music and comes from the heart. Write about something that is important to you.

My song is about:

Title:

Verse 1

Chorus

I ♥ HARRY — LIAM —

I ♥ ONE DIRECTION

Verse 2

Chorus

Verse 3

OUIS — NIAII & ZAYN

And The Award Goes To ...

The **1D** boys have had an amazing couple of years. Their talent and dedication has paid off and the boys are winning award after award! Here's a list of some of their major wins:

Winners
BRIT Award for Global Success 2013

BRIT Award for Best Single 2012 for 'What Makes You Beautiful'

BBC Radio One Teen Awards 2012: Best British Album, Best British Single, Best British Music Act

Nickelodeon Kids' Choice Awards 2012: Favourite UK Band, Favourite UK Newcomer

What awards could you win at school this year? Who will nominate you?

MTV Video Music Awards 2012: Best Pop Video, Best New Artist, Most Share-Worthy Video

Teen Choice Awards: Choice Music 2012: Breakout Group, Choice Summer Music Star: Group, Choice Music: Love Song for 'What Makes You Beautiful'

Award for best friend in the world because

....
....
....

Nominated by

....

Award for most improved student in

....

Nominated by

....

Award for top creative ideas in

....

Nominated by

....

Award for trying really hard in (even though it's not your fave subject)

....

Nominated by

....

4Music Video Honours 2012: Best Breakthrough, Best Group, Best Video 'What Makes You Beautiful'

27

What Makes You *Beautiful?*

**Some of the most beautiful things about people
are qualities that they don't often see in themselves.
Looking for the best in people is a great habit to have.**

*Some of the beautiful things that I love about my bffs
that they sometimes don't see in themselves are:*

Name: is beautiful because

Name: is beautiful because

Name: is beautiful because

Name: is beautiful because

Name: is beautiful because

Don't just think it, say it! Make sure you tell your besties how beautiful they are.

You might find it hard to see all the ways you shine but others will!

Some good things people say about me:

This is a pic of my beautiful friends!

If you get stuck you can ask your mum or a trusted friend to help you out.

SWEET TWEETS

We love hearing what the **1D** boys are thinking! Here are some of their top tweets:

ONE DIRECTION

 @Real_Liam_Payne
i hate watching myself i look so serious ha

 @zaynmalik
Wow this tour bus bed feels like heaven . . . :D. X

 @Harry_Styles
Today was the most amazing day I've had so far . . . in my life ever.

 @Louis_Tomlinson
Guys I've spent a lot of time reflecting this week on all we have achieved. I actually can't believe what you have helped us to achieve!

 @NiallOfficial
I destroyed a snackbox and a battered sausage last night!

 @zaynmalik
However many amazing things happen in your life you should always be thankful for it, remain humble, modest and respectful :) x

 @Harry_Styles
I slept on my shoulder, now my left arm is numb and is just hanging. It seems to be about 4 inches longer than my right. Cool.

 @NiallOfficial
Chillin havin a laugh! Great craic! Family and friends! That's what's up!

 @Louis_Tomlinson
Cut my toe surfing :(

 @Real_Liam_Payne
Hope everyone who has seen the tour has enjoyed it, love seeing everyone there singing along and dancing , amazinnggggg feeling !

My fave
1D
tweets are

....
....
....
....
....
....
....
....
....

I'm following:

Tour Guide

1D 3.

1D 2.

1D 4.

You don't need an A* in Geography to know that **1D** have done some serious globe-trotting in the last few years!

VIP PASS 1D

ACCESS ALL AREAS

Enter Ufa Door:2   **ONE D**
56788753547   One D
ONE DIRECTION   ONE D
PLUS
(VIP

Enter Ufa Door:2   **Enter**
56788753547   5678P
ONE DIRECTION

You have been signed up as the boys' new tour manager and your first job is to plan their latest tour. Find the cities named below on the map and plot your route by drawing a line between the cities.

New York

Paris

Stockholm

Sydney

Tokyo

Barcelona

Orlando

Toronto

London

Los Angeles

5.

6.

7.

8.

9. 1D

ONE DIRECTION
ONE DIRECTION
One Direction Presents
ONE DIRECTION
SPECIAL GUESTS
FRONT ROW
A78

10. 1D

Check your answers on page 90.

Tour Guide

Look at the postcards below and guess these famous cities where **1D** have wowed their fans.

1.

2.

3.

34

4.

Check your answers on page 90.

Time to plan your trip of a lifetime! Where would you like to visit? What sights would you go and see? Use the internet to research some of the places that 1D have visited so that you can follow in their footsteps.

Europe

The city I would most love

to visit is ....

While I'm there I'd love to see:

1. ....

2. ....

3. ....

The World

The city I would most love

to visit is ....

While I'm there I'd love to see:

1. ....

2. ....

3. ....

35

We know that you like to work hard and play hard, but how do you unwind? Think about all the stuff that you like to do outside of school, the things that help you to relax, and those activities that you have always wanted to try but haven't got round to yet.

Circle the activities that help you to unwind:

Relaxing in a bubble bath

Chillin' on the sofa with popcorn and a movie

Dancing to your fave **1D** *tunes*

Now add some
of your own:

My top 5 things to do in my free time are:

1.
2.
3.
4.
5.

Circle the activities that you most want to try:

Learn a musical instrument

Take a dance class

Sign up for a school play

Join a sports club

Now add some of your own:

I ♥ 1D

ONE DIRECTION WORDSEARCH

There are 15 words connected with **1D** below. Can you find them? They may be written forwards, backwards, up, down or diagonally.

D	E	Z	H	A	R	R	Y	B	F	E	S	J	I	Z
U	T	K	E	W	E	N	L	Q	U	E	S	T	S	A
E	H	A	R	N	T	O	U	R	C	R	E	B	O	Y
W	E	N	D	I	T	E	J	I	T	E	C	A	B	N
O	B	R	M	A	I	L	G	I	E	L	C	K	P	U
X	R	D	O	N	W	O	O	N	R	I	U	F	E	S
D	I	R	E	C	T	I	O	N	E	R	S	A	N	D
Y	T	C	O	R	X	U	C	I	M	E	Z	A	G	L
A	S	W	L	P	I	D	E	A	S	B	U	Y	N	L
J	U	I	T	S	I	U	O	L	S	O	E	D	I	V
K	O	T	E	D	U	W	A	L	E	L	R	W	H	O
Q	I	R	U	K	P	M	Y	G	N	N	C	U	T	E
H	U	R	O	T	C	A	F	X	E	H	T	Y	E	M
V	O	I	N	E	R	U	S	C	H	T	A	I	N	Y
P	A	L	T	F	E	I	L	E	R	C	I	M	O	C

HARRY
THE BRITS
LOUIS
THE X FACTOR
ONE THING
LIAM
TWITTER
DIRECTIONERS
TOUR
NIALL
SUCCESS
ZAYN
VIDEO
HIT
COMIC RELIEF

WORDS

Are you top of the **1D** class? How many words can you make from the word ...

ONE DIRECTION?

Because we're feeling kind we've started you off with a freebie! See how many words you can find and check your progress against the chart below.

1	Nice
2	
3	
4	
5	
6	
7	
8	
9	
10	
11	
12	
13	
14	
15	

Good start!

Good work!

Top of the class!

Check your answers on page 90.

School Notes

Are You A True Directioner?

Here are some quick questions to brush up on your band knowledge. Once you've taken the test, see if your friends are as **ID** smart as you!

I ♥ ONE DIRECTION

Quick Quiz

1. Which band member has got only one functioning kidney?
2. Who gave Niall a mug featuring a picture of him on the toilet?
3. What is Louis' middle name?
4. Which song on 'Take Me Home' was written by Ed Sheeran?
5. Which **ID** member has a grandad from Pakistan?
6. Whose birthday is on Christmas Eve?
7. Who has a tattoo of a microphone on their arm?
8. Whose home town is Holmes Chapel?

Check your answers on page 90.

Multiple Choice...

1. Harry's star sign is:
   a) Leo
   b) Aquarius
   c) Gemini

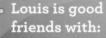
I ♥ HARRY

2. Niall's favourite colour is:
   a) Purple
   b) Red
   c) Green

I ♥ NIALL

3. Which band member was born prematurely?
   a) Niall
   b) Louis
   c) Liam

I ♥ LOUIS

4. Zayn's celebrity crush is:
   a) Megan Fox
   b) Nicole Kidman
   c) Angelina Jolie

I ♥ ZAYN

5. Louis is good friends with:
   a) Ryan Giggs
   b) Kylie Minogue
   c) James Corden

6. Who has a fear of birds flying indoors?
   a) Louis
   b) Harry
   c) Niall

I ♥ LIAM

7. Which 1D member has been known to wear his reindeer slippers on the tour bus?
   a) Zayn
   b) Louis
   c) Harry

Check your answers on page 91.

School Diary

September

October

November

I ❤ ONE DIRECTION

December

January

February

I ♥ ONE DIRECTION

March

April

May

June

July

August

SUPERSTAR STYLIN'

I ♥ 1D

Whether they are playing to the crowd on stage, or just hanging out together relaxing, the boys always look great!

All of the boys love their fashion! They easily mix designer threads and high street favourites to create their sharp stage looks.

I ♥ ONE DIRECTION

ONE DIRECTION

ONE DIRECTION

One Direction Presents

ONE DIRECTION
PLUS SPECIAL

NOW

Even just hanging out between performances and appearances they still know how to throw a hot look together.

Early Days

It's hard to imagine the boys before *The X Factor* rocketed them to interstellar stardom! Were they really ever ordinary boys? Did Harry work hard at school? Was Louis dreaming of stardom? Read the facts below and then imagine that you and your BFFs are destined for mega fame.

Harry
★ Was studying to become a lawyer – he's super-smart and gorgeous!
★ Worked part-time at the W. Mandeville Bakery in his home town when he was 16
★ When he was lead singer for White Eskimo they won a Battle of the Bands. Once a star, always a star!

Liam
★ Studied Music Technology at City of Wolverhampton College
★ Used to be a Scout
★ Performed in front of 26,000 people at a Wolverhampton Wanderers' match
★ Auditioned for *X Factor* in 2008, but Simon Cowell told him to come back in two years.

Louis
★ Was a waiter at a Vue Cinema and at Doncaster Rovers football stadium
★ Was a star in many musical productions at school, including *Grease*
★ Was in a TV drama called *If I Had You*.

Niall

★ Has played guitar as long as he can remember

★ Used to perform all over Ireland

★ Loved geography at school.

Zayn

★ Wanted to get an English degree and become a teacher

★ Had never been on a plane

★ Didn't have a passport.

ONE DIRECTION

What will the mags want to know about your life before fame came knocking?

My fave hobbies:

I was studying/working at:

My fave subject at school was:

My pet hate was:

My BFFs were :

My secret crush was:

Before we were famous we loved:

Now that we're famous our lives have changed because:

I Must Not Forget, I Must Not Forget...

When life is busy it's easy to lose track of important dates and deadlines. We know that you would be in big trouble if you forgot your best mate's birthday or missed handing in your homework! To help you plan ahead, fill in the boxes below.

I ♥ 1D

IMPORTANT

September
Birthdays to Remember:
....
....
....

Super Important Dates:
....
....

October
Birthdays to Remember:
....
....
....

Super Important Dates:
....
....

November
Birthdays to Remember:
....
....
....

Super Important Dates:
....
....

December
Birthdays to Remember:
....
....
....

Super Important Dates:
....
....

January
Birthdays to Remember:
....
....
....

Super Important Dates:
....
....

February
Birthdays to Remember:
....
....
....

Super Important Dates:
....
....

IMPORTANT

March
Birthdays to Remember:
....
....
Super Important Dates:
....
....

April
Birthdays to Remember:
....
....
Super Important Dates:
....
....

May
Birthdays to Remember:
....
....
Super Important Dates:
....
....

June
Birthdays to Remember:
....
....
Super Important Dates:
....
....

July
Birthdays to Remember:
....
....
Super Important Dates:
....
....

August
Birthdays to Remember:
....
....
Super Important Dates:
....
....

Lost Lyrics

I ♥ 1D

Just how well do you know 1D's hits? Time for you to prove that you are a 1D top-swot! Test your knowledge by completing the tasks below:

Name the songs that these mixed-up lyrics belong to?

1. *baby yeah take I'll you there*

2. *freckles joining and on I'm up cheeks the dots the with your*

3. *another one gonna way or see I'm ya*

4. *crazy let's 'til go crazy we see the crazy sun*

5. *I heart hear the louder beat of my getting*

6. *replay on replay she's on Katy Perry's*

7. *make-up cover need don't to up*

8. *you're me shot sky out of my kryptonite the*

What is the next line in the song?

9.   *You're turning heads when you walk through the door...*

10.   *Now girl I hear it in your voice and how it trembles...*

11.   *And find a girl and tell her she's the one...*

12.   *Come on and let me sneak you out...*

13.   *And if the lights are all out...*

What songs are these lines from?

14.   *I wanna hold you, wanna hold you tight*

15.   *Oh, tell me tell me tell me how to turn your love on*

16.   *And girl what a mess I made upon your innocence*

17.   *I die a little*

18.   *Being the way that you are is enough*

Check your answers on page 91.

Secret Crush

ONE DIRECTION

I ♡ _____ the most.

Because...

_____

_____

_____

_____

_____

_____

_____

_____

_____

_____

_____

_____

_____

_____

I ♥ ONE DIRECTION

I ♥ HARRY

stick a pic here!

Lush!

I ♥ ZAYN

Harry x

Lains x

stick a pic here!

1D

58

I ♥ LOUIS

Gorgeous!

Sweet!

stick a pic here!

stick a pic here!

I ♥ LIAM

I ♥ NIALL

MY BEST
BAND
MOMENTS

We know how much you love all things 1D but what are your top moments? It's hard to choose but see if you can pick out the memories that will stay with you.

It was so funny when ...

I loved it when ...

It's really nice when they ...

You could tell they really care about each other when ...

I thought _____ was the funniest when he ...

I wish I was there when ...

I ♥ 1D

My top 5 fave 1D moments:

1.

2.

3.

4.

5.

Say What?!

The 1D boys definitely have a way with words! Just how well do you know them? Can you guess who said what? Match the face to the words.

1. 'Just because you have the flaws, does not mean you aren't beautiful.'

2. 'We have a choice... to live or to exist.'

4. 'I don't know, it's odd that girls ask if they can hug me. Don't ask, do it. I'm just a regular guy.'

3. 'Before you judge people, judge yourself.'

Harry

Louis

5. 'Enjoy life, it has an expiration date.'

6. 'No matter how many times people try to criticize you, the best revenge is to prove them wrong.'

7. 'Live life for the moment because everything else is uncertain.'

8. 'I think you have to take me for me. I am who I am.'

9. 'I'll always defend the people I love.'

10. 'Believe it or not, but even when I'm sleeping, I'm dreaming about meeting fans.'

Check your answers on page 91.

Day Dream Diary

Date:

Dear Diary,

Dear Diary

I ♥ HARRY
LIAM
LOUIS
NIALL
ZAYN

MY TALENTS

We know that the One Direction boys are super-talented but what are your greatest gifts?

Harry

Liam

My main talent is:

My best subject at school is:

I'm good at it because:

My fave teacher says I'm good at:

My bestie loves me because:

When I leave school I want to:

The talents I am still working on are:

1.

2.

3.

Shhhhh! My secret talent that no one else knows about is:

LIGHTS, CAMERA, ACTION!

Title: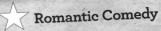

Genre:

- ★ Romantic Comedy
- ★ Weepie Chick Flick
- ★ Action
- ★ Sci-Fi
- ★ Horror

Time for your next challenge! You know those school assignments where you have to plan a project step by step? This is a super-fun version that you'll love doing!

The Brief:

We know it would be tough but if you absolutely HAD to write and star in a film with One Direction, what would it be like? Who would be your stars? How much money would you need to spend on glamorous sets, private jets and luxury hotels?

I ♥ ONE DIRECTION

Cast: Hot 1D co-stars:

Plot:

Start:

End:

Middle:

APPROVED

Budget:

£ _____ million

I ♥ ONE DIRECTION

Top School Favourites

We love knowing all the things that matter to the 1D boys! Knowing what makes them tick brings us closer to them. What were their fave things when they were at school? What challenges did they face?

Read all about the 1D boys' school days below and add the things that matter to you.

I ♥ LIAM

Favourite Subjects:

Harry: Maths, P.E.
Niall: French
Zayn: English, Art, Drama
Liam: P.E.
Louis: Drama

My fave subject is:

Top School Moments:

Louis: Starring in a school production of Grease
Zayn: Taking GCSE English a year early and getting an A!
Niall: Singing in the school choir

My top school moments so far:

I ♥ NIALL

School Challenges:

Niall: Struggled with English and Maths

Liam: Was bullied and took up boxing to build his confidence

Louis: Struggled to focus on his A-levels because he dreamed of being a star

My challenges to overcome are:

I ♥ LOUIS

I will work on these by:

My top ambitions are:

Top Ambitions:

Harry: Lawyer

Louis: Actor

Zayn: English teacher

I ♥ HARRY

This Year:

I ♥ ZAYN

Things I am looking forward to this year:

BFFs I will be hanging out with this year:

My fave teachers:

What I want to achieve:

Divas

The **1D** boys shouldn't be the only ones to get to conquer the globe in style with their best mates! Now it's your turn. There's nothing like a bit of girl power to rock the world. It's time to lay down your superstar plans for you and your besties.

Our band will be called:

Our stage names will be:

Our signature perfume will be called:

Our style of music will be:

Our fashion style will be:

Our first single will be called:

Our celebrity fans will be:

The countries we will visit on tour will be:

When we shoot to stardom we will:

75

My Album Art

I ♥ 1D

This is what I would have designed for the cover of *Up All Night*.

Is Art and Design your fave school subject? Get creative and make your own album covers by drawing, painting or sticking in cool images to make a collage. Remember it is about expressing how you feel about the music in pictures...

This is what I would design for the cover of my bands' first album.

BEING FAMOUS

Oh, the hard life of the famous!

Being flown around in a private jet, people bringing you whatever you want, sleeping all day until you have to go on stage... it sounds really terrible. Best to be prepared for when fame strikes!

The best things about being famous would be ....

....

....

The worst things about being famous would be ....

....

....

With all my piles of money I would buy ....

....

....

I ♥ ONE DIRECTION

The charity I would donate the most to is ....
....
....

My celebrity best friend would be ....
....
....

The city I would live in most of the time is...
....
....

But I'd also have a house/apartment in ....
....
....

Doesn't everyone dream of being famous? You've hit the big time and everyone wants to know what makes you tick. The requests for an interview come flooding in but you only talk to the coolest mags around.

If you were asked these questions by a glamorous magazine, what would you say?

What do you love most about being famous?

....
....
....
....
....

What do you love least about being famous?

....
....
....
....
....

You've been on tour for a while. What's your favourite thing about going home?

....
....
....
....

What's your craziest tour story?

....
....
....
....
....
....

What's it like to travel the world with your best friends?

....
....
....
....
....

Where do you want to tour next?

....
....
....
....
....
....

What's your fave city?

....
....
....
....
....
....

What's your fave after-show snack?

....
....
....
....
....
....

Who is your inspiration?

....
....
....
....
....
....

Do you have any diva demands?

....
....
....
....
....

What band do you want to tour with the most?

....
....
....
....
....
....

Dream Holiday

Imagine your dream comes true and you get to plan your perfect holiday, complete with the boys to keep you entertained. Choose from the options below to create the perfect scene to remember.

My dream holiday with **ONE DIRECTION** would be:

☐ On an island
☐ In a glamorous city
☐ A countryside retreat

☐ By the beach
☐ Camping at a festival
☐ Other

I would pack:

I wouldn't leave without:

The friends I would take are:

I would want to go by:

☐ Plane
☐ Private jet
☐ Car

☐ Helicopter
☐ Yacht
☐ Speedboat

☐ Train
☐ Bicycle

Super School Term Planner

Every school term is different and comes with its particular pressures and excitements. Think about the things that you want to get out of your school year by focusing on it term by term.

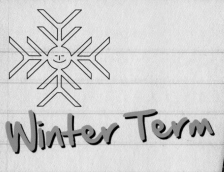

Winter Term

Top 3 things I want to achieve this term:

1.

2.

3.

What I am most looking forward to:

Things that will challenge me:

1.

2.

3.

Ways that I will overcome these challenges:

1.

2.

3.

Spring Term

Top 3 things I want to achieve this term:

1.

2.

3.

What I am most looking forward to:

Things that will challenge me:

1.

2.

3.

Ways that I will overcome these challenges:

1.

2.

3.

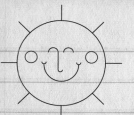

Summer Term

Top 3 things I want to achieve this term:

1.

2.

3.

What I am most looking forward to:

Things that will challenge me:

1.

2.

3.

Ways that I will overcome these challenges:

1.

2.

3.

My **1D** Party

Make your next sleepover a **1D**-themed party! Follow these cool tips to turn it into a memorable night ...

Food

Delicious food is very important. Make sure there are some healthy options and check if anyone has a food allergy before the party.

*Try some of the **1D** boys' fave dishes, like pasta, pizza and ice cream. Mmmmmm!*

Let's party everybody ★

Decorations

Get everyone to bring their favourite posters and pics of the band and stick them up all over the room (with your parents' or guardians' permission of course!)

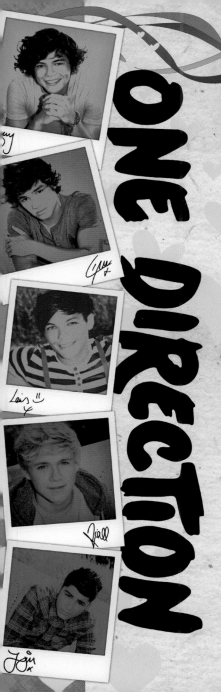

Games & Music

Of course the band of the night will be on the playlist. But to mix it up a little, cut up some scraps of paper and get everyone to write down their fave **1D** track. Count up the votes in secret and then play your guests' choices in order of popularity, so you end with everyone's fave song at number one!

Now you know which song your BFFs love the most, make up some funky dance moves to go with it. It's a good excuse to play your fave song on repeat!

Give classic games a **1D** twist! For example, for a **1D** pass-the-parcel, add a note with a question on each layer, such as 'Which band member said that he loves Maltesers?' When the music stops, the person with the parcel has to answer the question correctly to be able to open the layer. Or if they get it wrong, they could choose a truth or dare option! Make the final present inside a **1D** themed gift.

Thank you!

Take loads of pics of your BFFs throughout the party. Afterwards you can print the pics and write nice notes on the back to thank everyone for coming!

ANSWERS

Page 20

1. *Tell Me A Lie*
2. *More Than This, Taken, and Stole My Heart*
3. *13*

Page 32-33

1. *Toronto, Canada*
2. *Los Angeles, USA*
3. *New York, USA*
4. *Orlando, USA*
5. *London, UK*
6. *Stockholm, Sweden*
7. *Paris, France*
8. *Barcelona, Spain*
9. *Tokyo, Japan*
10. *Sydney, Australia*

Page 34

1. *London, UK*
2. *Los Angeles, USA*
3. *Paris, France*
4. *Tokyo, Japan*

Page 38

D	E	Z	H	A	R	R	Y	B	F	E	S	J	I	Z
U	T	K	E	W	E	N	L	Q	U	E	S	T	S	A
E	H	A	R	N	T	O	U	R	C	R	E	B	O	Y
W	E	N	D	I	T	E	J	I	T	E	C	A	B	N
O	B	R	M	A	I	L	G	I	E	L	C	K	P	U
X	R	D	O	N	W	O	O	N	R	I	U	F	E	S
D	I	R	E	C	T	I	O	N	E	R	S	A	N	D
Y	T	C	O	R	X	U	C	I	M	E	Z	A	G	L
A	S	W	L	P	I	D	E	A	S	B	U	Y	N	L
J	U	I	T	S	I	U	O	L	S	O	E	D	I	V
K	O	T	E	D	U	W	A	L	E	L	R	W	H	O
Q	I	R	U	K	P	M	Y	G	N	N	C	U	T	E
H	U	R	O	T	C	A	F	X	E	H	T	Y	E	M
V	O	I	N	E	R	U	S	C	H	T	A	I	N	Y
P	A	L	T	F	E	I	L	E	R	C	I	M	O	C

Page 39

Possible answers: ride, nine, dire, none, nerd, tire, red, rode, done, neon, direct, drone, cite, tree

Page 42

1. *Liam*
2. *Harry*
3. *William*
4. *'Little Things'*
5. *Zayn*
6. *Louis*
7. *Zayn*
8. *Harry*

I ♥ 1D

90

I ♥ ONE DIRECTION

Page 43

1. b
2. a
3. c
4. a
5. c
6. c
7. b

Page 54-55

1. Baby I'll take you there, yeah 'Kiss You'
2. And I'm joining up the dots with the freckles on your cheeks 'Little Things'
3. One way or another I'm gonna see ya 'One Way Or Another (Teenage Kicks)'
4. Let's go crazy, crazy, crazy 'til we see the sun 'Live While We're Young'
5. I hear the beat of my heart getting louder 'I Wish'
6. Katy Perry's on replay/She's on replay 'Up All Night'
7. Don't need make-up/ To cover up 'What Makes You Beautiful'
8. Shot me out of the sky/You're my kryptonite 'One Thing'
9. Don't need make up 'What Makes You Beautiful'
10. When you speak to me I don't resemble who I was 'Gotta Be You'
11. Hold on to the feeling 'Up All Night'
12. And have a celebration, a celebration 'Live While You're Young'
13. I'll follow your bus downtown 'One Way Or Another (Teenage Kicks)'
14. 'One Way Or Another (Teenage Kicks)'
15. 'Kiss Me'
16. 'Gotta Be You'
17. 'I Wish'
18. 'What Makes You Beautiful'

Page 62-63

1. Zayn
2. Harry
3. Zayn
4. Niall
5. Zayn
6. Zayn
7. Louis
8. Harry
9. Niall
10. Liam

ONE DIRECTION

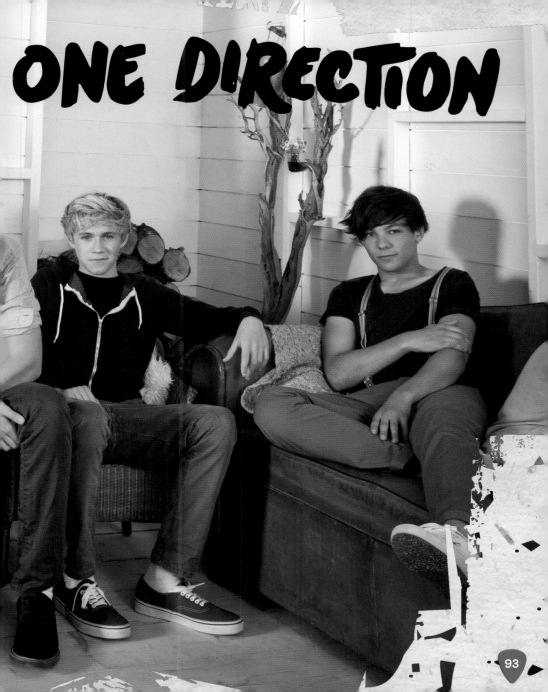

I ♥ 1D

Harry